Billy Conker's

NATURE-SPOTTING ADVENTURE

Conor Busuttil

THE O'BRIEN PRESS
DUBLIN

Hi, I'm Billy Conker!

I love exploring our natural world and finding ways to help and protect all the wildlife I come across. I think you're never too young to make a difference. Me, I've been a conservationist since before I even knew what that meant! My backpack is full of adventure gear, and I can't wait to share my travels with you.

We're going in search of the creatures that need us the most, from tiny starfish to great grizzly bears, and we'll talk about ways we can help them to survive.

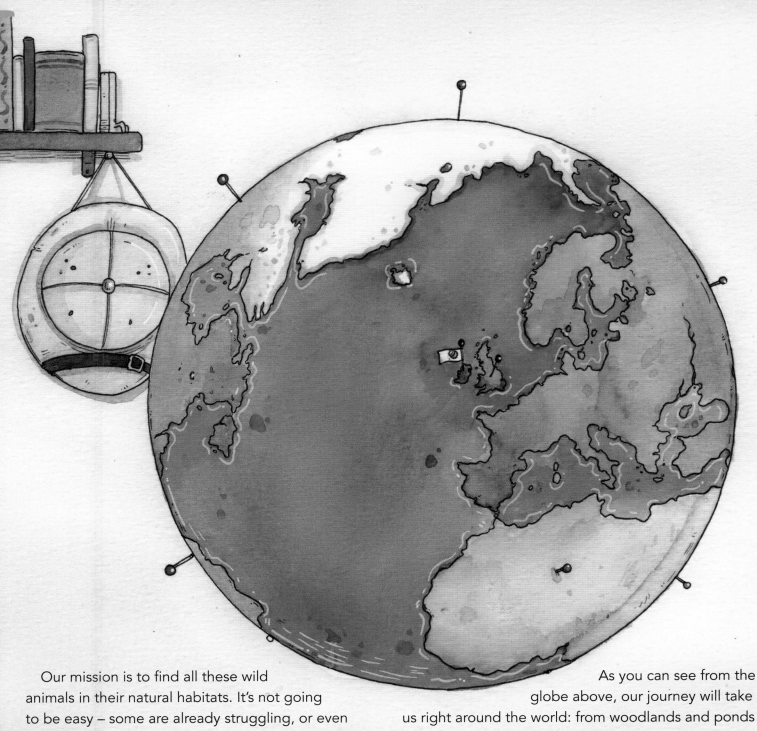

Our mission is to find all these wild animals in their natural habitats. It's not going to be easy — some are already struggling, or even endangered, and these are the hardest to find. Use the explorer's checklist to discover just a few of the creatures that live in each ecosystem.

As you can see from the globe above, our journey will take us right around the world: from woodlands and ponds to snow-covered mountain peaks, from the mysterious rainforest to the deep blue ocean, from the barren desert to the buzzing city.

Are you ready? Backpacks on, eyes peeled ... Let's go!

Billy's Garden

Where else would we start our adventure but in my own back garden? Lots of amazing creatures live right beside us – but they need a little encouragement to come and visit! By making a small hole in a fence, we welcome in hungry hedgehogs. And by planting nectar-producing flora (flowers), we attract busy bees and other insects, which in turn draw birds and other small fauna (animals).

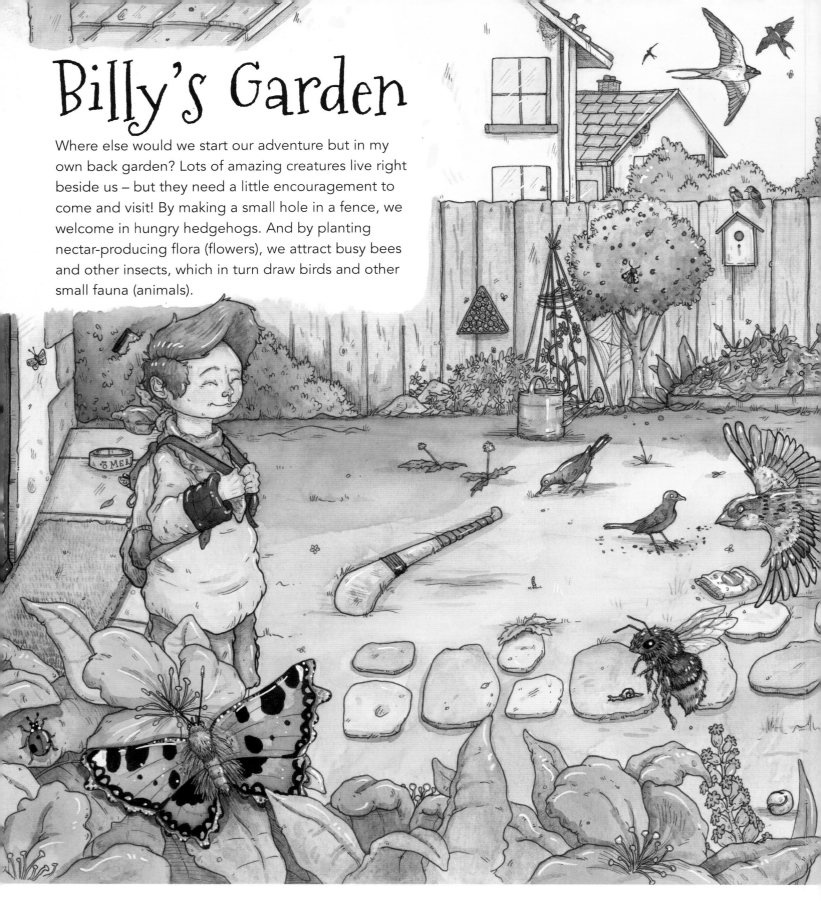

Here's your explorer's checklist. Try to find all ten creatures plus the endangered species – this might be the trickiest one. Remember that some animals might be hiding, or they might be in a different pose. And look out for any man-made items scattered around!

Swallow

Red-tailed Bumblebee

Common Blue Butterfly

Small Tortoiseshell Butterfly

House
Mouse

Garden
Spider

Blackbird

Common
Toad

Garden
Tiger Moth

House
Sparrow

Hedgehog

ENDANGERED SPECIES

Woodland

Our wonderful woods have lots of hiding places, so animals feel safe here! Below the ground, in the 'field', or high in the tree canopy, you'll find mammals and amphibians, insects and birds. (Look out for my owl friend Shortie, who is passing through on his morning hunt!) If tree cover is dense, with lots of dark and damp spots, it is also a perfect home for plants we wouldn't find elsewhere such as ferns or fungi (mushrooms).

Pine Marten

ENDANGERED SPECIES

Blue Tit

Red Fox

Badger

Rabbit

Red Squirrel

Mole

Short-eared Owl

Red Deer Stag

Nuthatch

Goshawk

DID YOU KNOW?

Trees use an underground network of fungi –
like a 'wood-wide web' – to communicate and share
water and nutrients. They even send each other
distress signals!

Pond

A pond is an inland body of fresh water, kind of like a small lake. And it holds lots of secrets! From where I'm perched, it looks quiet and still – but under the water, there is a thriving ecosystem of plants and creatures living together. There are even more species living in the muddy margins and the vegetation around the edges. Unfortunately, ponds can also hide a lot of rubbish. Keep an eye out for litter, and we'll take it back home when we leave!

DID YOU KNOW?

We all change a bit as we get older, but some creatures go through extreme changes – it's called 'metamorphosis'. Our frog pal here starts as an egg in spawn, then changes into a legless tadpole, then into a fully grown, lilypad-leaping adult!

Otter

Pike

Dragonfly

Eel

Water Vole

ENDANGERED SPECIES

Newt

Common Frog

Heron

Water Boatman

Beaver

Stickleback

Tundra

A tundra is a freezing, windy, treeless region found in the Arctic and on the tops of mountains. It doesn't get much rain, so it's like a very cold desert! The animals living here have adapted to long, cold winters – some have an extra layer of fat, and some hibernate or migrate during the coldest months. Plants are low to the ground and grouped together for protection from the sweeping winds. We'll need our big coats for this adventure!

Polar Bear

ENDANGERED SPECIES

Walrus

Arctic Hare

Arctic Fox

Orca

Musk Ox

Gyrfalcon

Rock Ptarmigan

DID YOU KNOW?

In order to stay hidden within their habitat, the Arctic hare and Arctic fox change from snowy white in winter to earthy brown in the warmer months.

Reindeer   Harp Seal   Narwhal

Prairie

Here we are in the grassland prairie, where the landscape changes from wide, flat strips of grass to rolling hills, and from tall, coniferous forests to snow-capped mountains. In this vast space, many animals move in groups for strength – we can see herds of grazing bison and packs of grey wolves. The weather is scorching hot in the summer months and brutally cold in winter, so it takes teamwork to survive!

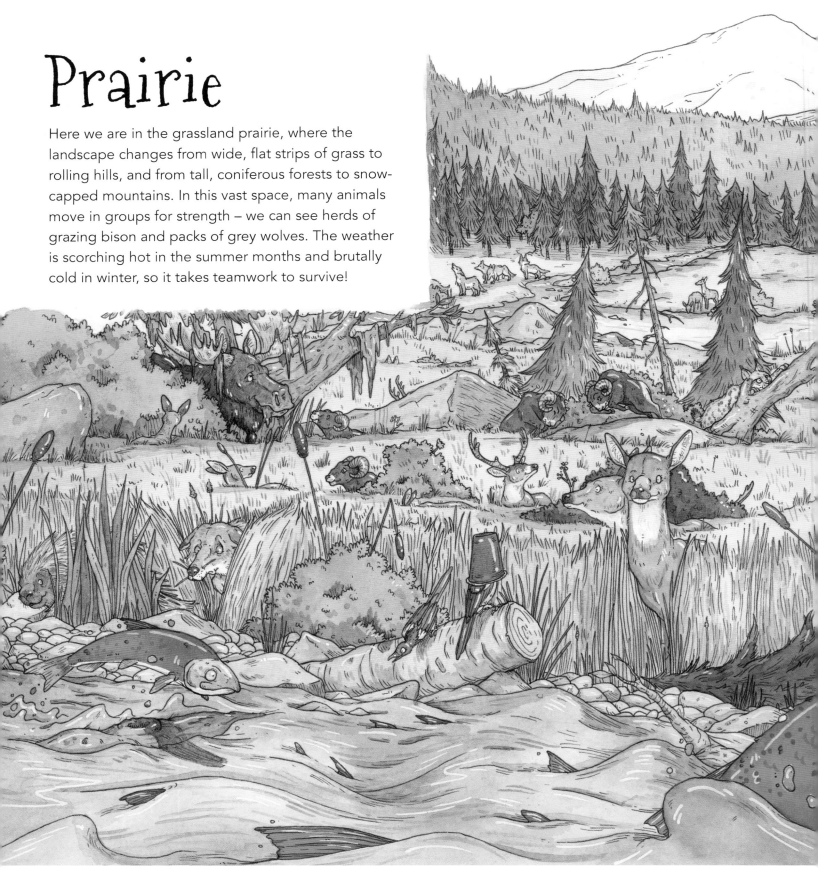

DID YOU KNOW?

The lynx is a medium-sized wild cat that has large, round feet to help it travel across the thick snow – a bit like those snow shoes that look like tennis racquets!

American Bison

Bald Eagle

Black-tailed Prairie Dog

Coyote

Grey Wolf

Grizzly Bear

ENDANGERED SPECIES

Lynx   Moose   Porcupine   Sockeye   Sandhill Crane
                              Salmon

Ocean

Down we go, into the glorious blue depths! The ocean covers an incredible 70% of the Earth's surface, and it is a home and food source for fish, mammals, plants, birds and more. Most creatures here swim in groups: fish in shoals, dolphins in pods. The mighty Blue Whale prefers to travel alone, so even though it's huge, it can be hard to spot! The ocean absorbs heat from the sun, so as the planet warms, the water warms too, which is putting marine life in danger.

Blue Whale

ENDANGERED SPECIES

Blue-footed Booby

Bottle-nosed Dolphin

Bull Shark

Giant Squid

Humpback Whale

Leatherback Turtle

Manta R

DID YOU KNOW?

Sea creatures often work together to round up their prey. Here, the birds drop from above, the dolphin comes in from the side and the whales from below – the small fish form a 'bait ball' for protection.

Marlin

Sardine

Sunfish

Desert

Phew! It is seriously hot here, and we've found the only water for miles around. It's places like this, though, that show how amazing nature is – animals have again adapted and found ways to survive! Clever plants called succulents store water in their leaves, stems and roots, and the animals eat them to quench their thirst. They also get moisture from their prey, and some burrow down deep and sleep while the sun is at its hottest.

DID YOU KNOW?

Scientists are looking into ways to turn parts of the world's deserts into giant solar farms, which would create enough energy to replace fossil fuels around the world.

Arabian Camel

Desert Hedgehog

Fennec Fo

Egyptian Tortoise

ENDANGERED SPECIES

Horned Viper · Oryx · Ostrich · Rock Hyrax · Deathstalker Scorpion · Tawny Eagle · Desert Jerboa

Mountain

What a mysterious place the mountain is. You wouldn't think many creatures could survive its cold, icy winds and lack of food. But in fact, it is the ideal home for solitary animals like the elusive snow leopard. Some animals here are so good at hide-and-seek that conservationists (people working to protect animals, like you and me) have to set up special cameras to keep an eye on them!

Snow Leopard

ENDANGERED SPECIES

Ibex Goat

Yak

Monal Pheasant

Himalayan Black Bear

Red Panda

Golden Snub-nosed Monkey

Bharal

DID YOU KNOW?

To survive in the cold, thin mountain air, my yak friend has a larger heart and lungs than a cow or buffalo. He has thick skin, thick hair, and he doesn't sweat!

Himalayan
Macaque

Pika

Griffon
Vulture

Savannah

Here we are in the savannah, a tropical grassland with large plains and scattered trees. Because it's so open, with few places to hide, many of the animals here rely on camouflage (blending in with their surroundings) to survive – we'll really have to search for those ones! The savannah has extreme wet and dry seasons; during the dry season, plants wither and food is scarce, so some animals migrate or hibernate until the rains come again.

DID YOU KNOW?

Elephants and rhinos have tusks (large teeth) made of ivory, which is worth a lot of money. Thousands of these animals are poached each year, putting them in danger of extinction.

Aardvark

African Elephant

Giraffe

Black Rhino

ENDANGERED SPECIES

Lappet-faced Vulture

African Lion

Spotted Hyena

Thomson's Gazelle

Hippo

Cheetah

Termite

City

This place is so dusty and noisy and full of people that it's the last place you'd expect to see wildlife. But nature always finds a way! Many of the animals here have adapted to urban life, finding scraps of food and homes amongst the tall buildings. We can encourage flora to grow and fauna to visit by 'greening' our cities: adding parks and community gardens, or even just spots of green on our roofs and windowsills.

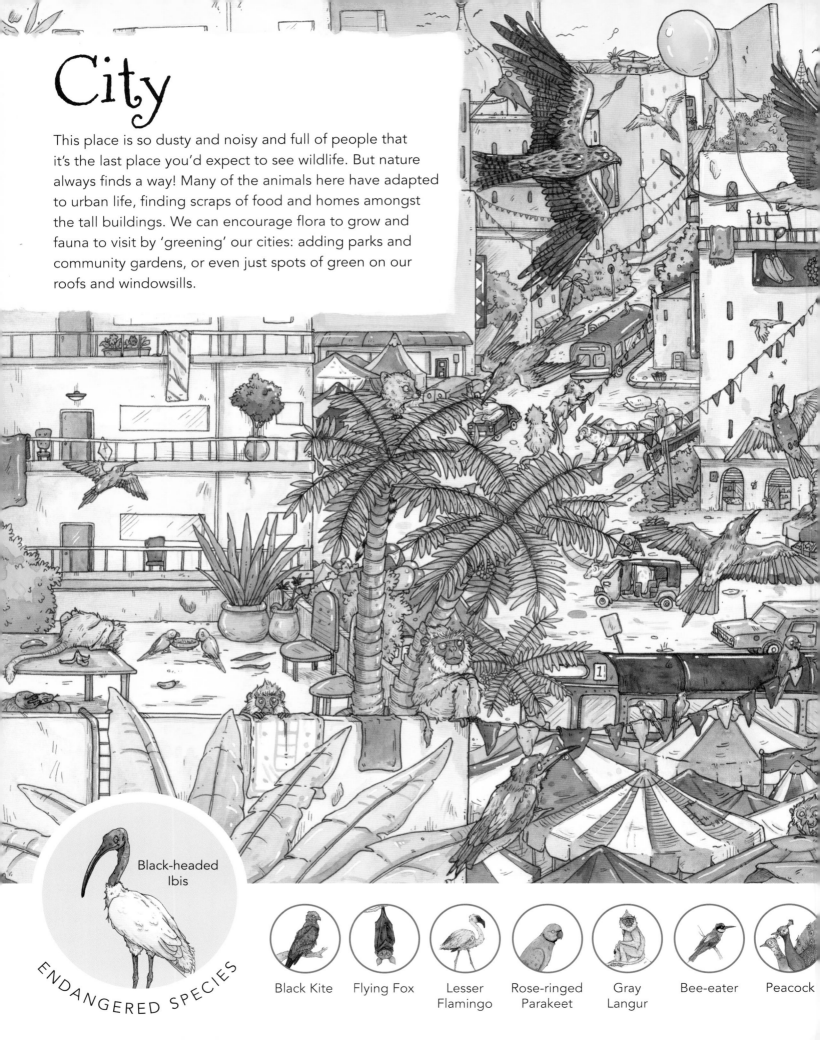

Black-headed Ibis

ENDANGERED SPECIES

Black Kite

Flying Fox

Lesser Flamingo

Rose-ringed Parakeet

Gray Langur

Bee-eater

Peacock

DID YOU KNOW?

To keep themselves safe from humans, some city-dwelling animals have become nocturnal – moving most of their activity from the day into the dark hours of the night.

Ox

Small Indian Civet

Leopard

Rainforest

I love the rainforest – it's like nature's city, brimming with weird and wonderful wildlife. With so many tall trees around, some animals adapt to life in the treetops, while those on the ground find special ways to either hide or make themselves stand out. Some of the birds here will sing, dance or use optical illusions to attract a mate!

DID YOU KNOW?

Rainforests are under threat from deforestation, where trees are cut down not just for wood but to make way for mining, drilling, palm-oil plantations or grazing cattle.

Coatimundi

Three-toed Sloth

Red-eyed Tree Frog

Tapir

Blue-and-
yellow Macaw

Toucan

Red Howler
Monkey

Green
Anaconda

Black Spider
Monkey

Giant Otter

Jaguar

ENDANGERED SPECIES

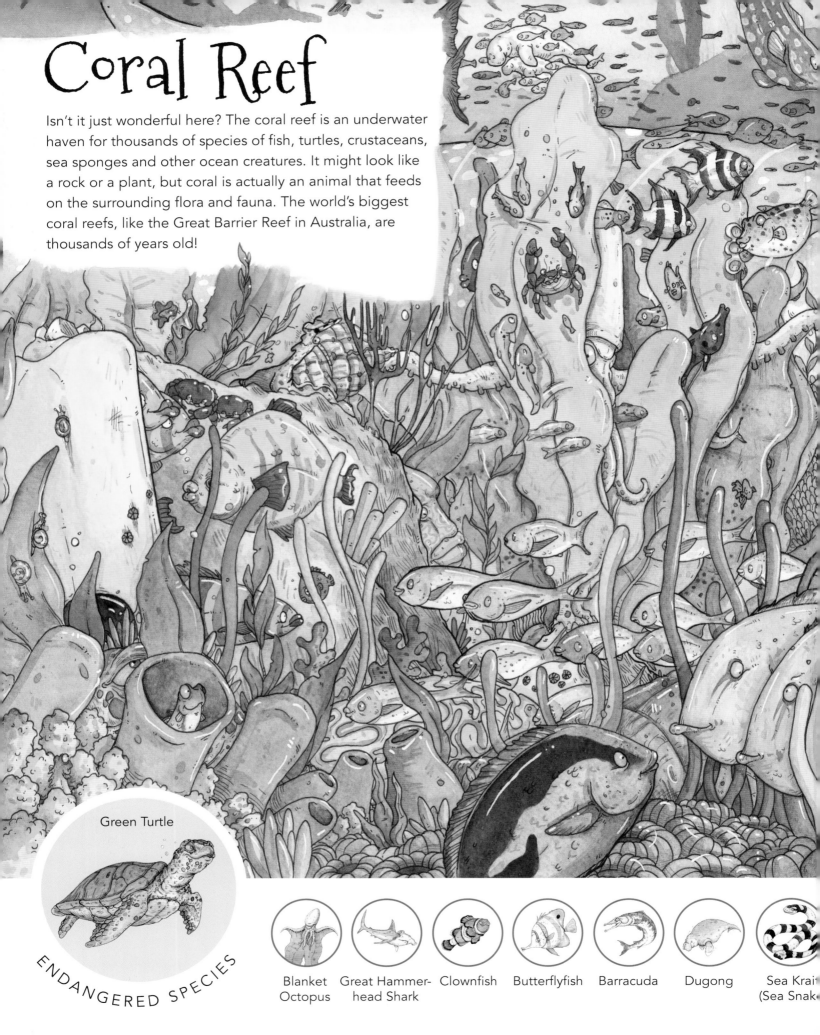

Coral Reef

Isn't it just wonderful here? The coral reef is an underwater haven for thousands of species of fish, turtles, crustaceans, sea sponges and other ocean creatures. It might look like a rock or a plant, but coral is actually an animal that feeds on the surrounding flora and fauna. The world's biggest coral reefs, like the Great Barrier Reef in Australia, are thousands of years old!

Green Turtle

ENDANGERED SPECIES

Blanket Octopus

Great Hammer-head Shark

Clownfish

Butterflyfish

Barracuda

Dugong

Sea Krait (Sea Snake)

DID YOU KNOW?

Even the tiniest rise in sea temperature can cause bleaching, where the coral loses its lovely, vibrant colour.

Whale Shark   Humphead Wrasse   Giant Triton Snail

Our Planet and Us

The world is so beautiful, and I love visiting all these amazing places and sneaking a peek at the creatures living there. But as you can see from our adventures, the choices that humans make every day can have a negative effect on nature too.

Deforestation

This means chopping down trees for wood or to make way for buildings, growing crops or raising farm animals. Although new trees are being planted, many more are disappearing, so it's hard to catch up. To help, I try not to use too much paper, and I recycle what I use. I also eat lots of plant-based foods (made from fruit, veggies, grains and nuts) that are produced locally.

Rubbish

People buy a lot of stuff these days, and not all of it can be recycled. Much ends up on huge landfill sites and can take a long time to wear away. I try not to buy too much new stuff, and I reuse or pass along the things I don't need anymore. I also recycle as much as possible. Recycling takes old things like plastic bottles and tin cans, melts them down and turns them into other products so they never end up on these big piles.

Pollution

Some of the rubbish we throw away finds its way into our rivers, lakes and oceans. This can be dangerous for the fish and other animals that live there – they might swallow things they find, or they could get tangled up in debris. I try to buy eco-friendly products instead of plastic ones, and I recycle as much as I can. And whenever I see some rubbish where it's not supposed to be, I pick it up!

Energy

Fossil fuels (that's coal, oil and gas) are used to heat homes and factories and run cars and planes, and they release harmful greenhouse gases into the Earth's lovely air. Every day, people are coming up with new ways to harness clean, reusable energy, like solar panels for your house and electric cars, buses and bikes. Young conservationists like you and me can join the effort one day! And in the meantime, we can turn off lights and electronics when they aren't being used and try to conserve water.

Other Ways to Help

As well as making clever choices about recycling, using energy and what we buy, there's plenty we can do to help our local environment, and it all starts at home!

Plant

Having plants, flowers and trees around makes us feel happier, and it also attracts wildlife. Bees and other insects will come, followed by birds and other animals such as hedgehogs and badgers, if you're lucky! This is what we call a 'food chain', with one species feeding or looking after another species. If you don't have an outdoor space, you can fill window-boxes and pots with bee-friendly flowers – or maybe you and your class could do some planting at school!

Welcome the Neighbours

We want to encourage wildlife into our gardens, but sometimes we forget to leave the door open! We put fences and walls up to keep our pets in, but this also keeps some wildlife out. With a grownup's permission, make a saucer-sized hole in the garden fence, which should allow the likes of a hedgehog to pass from garden to garden, gobbling up slugs and grubs to its heart's content.

Bed and Breakfast

Bird houses and feeders bring in lots of visitors, giving them a place to nest and lay eggs in the warmer months and a source of food in the colder months. Bug and bee hotels, which are wooden houses with small, cosy holes, make the perfect home for creepy crawlies.

Pedal power

'Do I need a lift, or could I walk or cycle instead?' That's the conservationist's way of thinking! Avoiding the car is better for the planet, and it's healthier. Besides, I love zooming around on my scooter!

Dedication

To my dearest Kat, forever and always my guiding Star

Acknowledgements

Many thanks to all involved, but a special mention to: Ben Hoare for his extensive knowledge of the animal kingdom; Paul Westmoreland for his wordsmith mastery; the Arts Council of Ireland for their continued support; Emma, Nicola and all the O'Brien Press team; and my agent Gill at Bath Literary Agency for being the driving force behind this project.

About the Author

Conor Busuttil is a children's picture book illustrator and a lover of all things nature. Growing up in a small country village on the Strangford Lough coast in County Down, he spent many a day exploring the marshy farmlands for tadpoles and newts, and the rocky coastline in search of the mysterious creatures the tide left behind in its seaweedy pools. To be able to create this book has been a dream come true for Conor, and he only hopes you enjoy reading it as much as he enjoyed working on it.

First published 2022 by
The O'Brien Press Ltd, 12 Terenure Road East, Rathgar, Dublin 6, D06 HD27, Ireland.
Tel: +353 1 4923333; Fax: +353 1 4922777; E-mail: books@obrien.ie; Website: obrien.ie
The O'Brien Press is a member of Publishing Ireland.

ISBN: 978-1-78849-284-3

8 7 6 5 4 3 2 1
26 25 24 23 22

Printed and bound in Poland by Bialostockie Zaklady Graficzne S.A.
The paper in this book is produced using pulp from managed forests.

Billy Conker's Nature-Spotting Adventure receives financial assistance from the Arts Council.

Published in

DUBLIN
UNESCO
City of Literature

Growing up with
O'BRIEN
obrien.ie